£5.99

Twinkle

2003

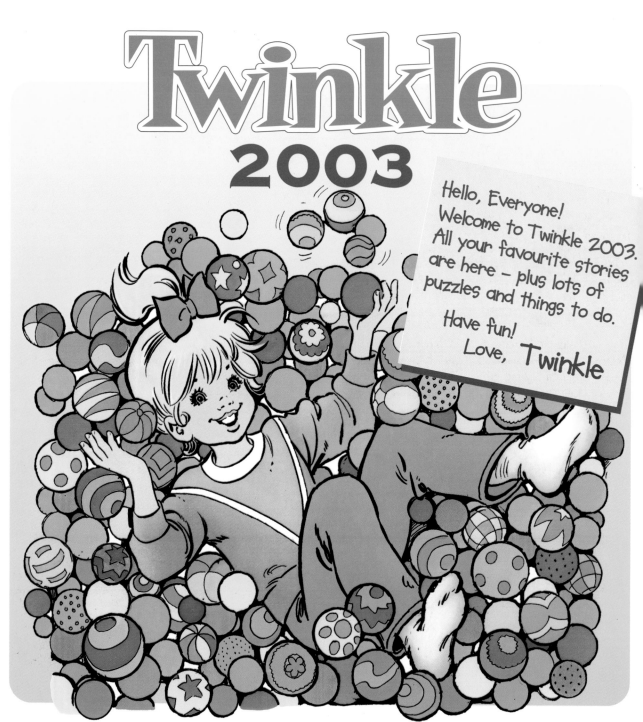

Hello, Everyone!
Welcome to Twinkle 2003.
All your favourite stories
are here – plus lots of
puzzles and things to do.

Have fun!

Love, Twinkle

Printed and published by D. C. Thomson & Co. Ltd., Dundee & London

ISBN 0 85116 814 0

Nurse Nancy

1 — It was almost Christmas, and Nurse Nancy and Grandad were hard at work in the hospital trying to make sure all the toys would be home for Christmas Day.

2 — However, some toys wouldn't be well enough to go home, and their owners were sad. To cheer up the ward, Nancy decided to put up some decorations.

3 — On Christmas Eve, the boys and girls came to the hospital to say "goodbye" to their toys. As tomorrow was Christmas Day, they would be too busy to visit them.

4 — Next day, Nancy had a lovely time with lots of super presents. "I'll go in to the hospital later to check on the patients, Grandad," said Nancy.

5 — At the hospital, the patients looked sad. Then Nancy smiled. "I know what we'll do," she cried. "We'll have another Christmas tomorrow!"

6 — When Nancy returned home, Mummy was busy clearing the dinner table. "Can I have the leftovers, Mummy?" Nancy asked. "I'm having a Christmas party!" Mummy **was** puzzled!

7 — That evening, Nancy was very busy wrapping up small Christmas presents for the toys, and telling all her friends about the special party the following day.

8 — Next day, Nancy set off early to the hospital with food and presents. All her friends brought things, too — everyone was really looking forward to the party.

9 — All Nancy's chums had great fun at the party — and so did the patients. They played games, opened their presents and then they all had a lovely Christmas meal.

10 — "It's a super idea having two Christmas Days," said Tom, whose teddy was in with a sore paw. "I think we should do it again next year!" Everyone agreed.

Sara and Sam

It was Sara's birthday and she was very excited.

"That's the postman with my cards now," she squealed as she heard lots of cards plop onto the mat. "I can't wait to open them!"

There were cards from all her friends and one from Mummy and Daddy.

Sam had made a card all by himself and Sara thought it was very pretty. "Thank you, Sam," she said to her little brother. "I think your card is the prettiest of all." Sam **was** pleased.

But suddenly Sara stopped. "There isn't a card from Grandpa," she gasped. "I hope he hasn't forgotten."

"Of course I haven't forgotten," said a voice. Sara looked up to see Grandpa coming into the room wearing a huge smile and carrying the biggest card she had ever seen. "My card was too big to put through your letterbox, so I brought it round myself."

Sara opened the huge card and gave a gasp of surprise as it began to play her favourite tune. "It's a musical birthday card," cried Sara. "Oh, Grandpa, it's lovely! I think my cards are the best cards ever!"

Later some of Sara's friends came round for tea. "We can play games," said Sara. "What about musical chairs? " Everyone agreed, so Daddy found a tape and put it in the tape player.

All the children danced round the chairs. Then, when the music stopped, they dashed to find a chair. It was great fun. But then, when there were only four left in the game, the music stopped all

on its own. "There's something wrong with the tape," exclaimed Sam.

Daddy came to look at it. "I'm afraid the player is broken," he said. Everyone was very disappointed because they couldn't finish their game.

Then Sam jumped up! "We could use this," he cried, holding up Sara's musical card.

And the card was just right for the game. When Sam opened it the music played, and when he closed it the music stopped and everyone dashed to find a chair. The children were still playing when Grandpa came back. "I'm glad I brought Sara that card," he chuckled. And so was everyone else.

1 - Paula Perkins has a cute kitten called Patch. He likes to join in whatever Paula does. When Paula's friend, Sarah, brought a puppy to visit, Patch was ready to have fun.

2 - Ember, the puppy, wanted to play, but not with Patch. **She** only wanted to play with Patch's toys. She collected them all into a pile and wouldn't let Patch have any.

3 - Paula and Sarah laughed, but Patch didn't think it was funny. Every time he tried to play with a toy, Ember snatched it away. She even chased Patch when he picked up a pom-pom!

4 - Later, Paula and Sarah brought out a basket of wool. "Now, now," scolded Sarah as Patch and Ember tried to play with the balls, "we don't want it tangled."

5 - But when Paula and Sarah left the room, the pets had a super time chasing the wool **and** each other. They had found a game they could **both** play!

6 - What a mess the girls found when they returned - but Patch and Ember were fast asleep. That was something **else** they could do together!

Peter's Puzzles

Peter's put together two pages of winter puzzles – just for you

You can colour this picture using your pens, paints or crayons.

These bears are dressed like Christmas fairies.
Which two are exactly the same?

Answer: 1 and 4

r a c
k e
r c

Wow! Re-arrange these letters to see what the bears are pulling!

Answer: Cracker.

Whee! Lead Peter through the maze to his pals!

There are six differences between these two pictures. Can you spot them?

Join the dots to see the teddies' Christmas presents!

Baby Brother's Year

In **January**, there's lots of snow
   Upon the frozen ground.
Ben makes a snowman tall and proud,
   The best for miles around.

In **February**, Ben runs to pick
   The catkins, soft and yellow.
"The lambs have tails like catkins, too!"
   Exclaims the little fellow.

The wind blows merrily in **March**,
   The sun is shining bright.
"Let's march up to the hill!" laughs Ben.
   "I want to fly my kite!"

One **April** day, I think I hear
   A cuckoo's springtime call.
But it is just that cheeky boy
   And not a bird at all!

The pretty bluebells bloom in **May**
　　And so back home we bring
A little bunch from Ben to Mum.
　　He grins, "Why don't they ring?"

In **June** we go out picnicking
　　With strawberries for tea.
Somehow, the rascal always gets
　　The biggest ones, not me!

July is when we holiday
　　Down by the sea we go.
Ben jumps into his swimming trunks
　　And dips in his big toe!

In **August**, it is harvest time,
　　There's plenty to be done.
But like Boy Blue, Ben falls asleep
　　And snoozes in the sun.

September brings ripe apples and
    They look so sweet and red.
Ben tries to shake one down - oh, dear!
    It lands upon his head!

October - days of falling leaves.
    Ben sweeps them in a pile,
But *whoosh* the wind blows them away!
    I try to hide a smile!

November means Guy Fawkes, of course
    When fireworks light the sky.
"I like the rockets best," says Ben.
    "Just watch how high they fly!"

December, and it's Christmas time.
    "A Merry Christmas, Sis!"
Cries Ben as he runs up to me
    And plants a soppy kiss!

My Baby Brother
cut-out

Here's Ben and his favourite cowboy outfit. To dress him up, cut round the thick black lines of both Ben and his outfit, taking care at the tabs (an adult can help you with this). Stick the page onto card, if you like, before cutting out. Place the outfit over the figure and bend the tabs over to keep it in place. Bend the base at the dotted line and the figure will stand up. To fit the hat, cut across the dotted line and slip the hat on Ben's head. And there he is – Ben the Cowboy!

The Blobs

...bright little blobs of paint who come out of a paintbox into the wonderful world of Paintbox Land.

Powder Blue was walking along the lane past Inky Black's house.

"Hello!" she called to the witch. "What are you doing?"

"Getting Whispers ready for the Pet Show," smiled Inky.

Whispers didn't look particularly happy about all the grooming that was going on, but he stood still with his tail twitching.

"There! You look much better now," crooned the old crone, looking proudly at her favourite moggy. "Now, you have

to keep clean so you look your best this afternoon. No lying in the flowerbeds or rolling yourself in some dusty corner. Understood?"

Whispers wanted to do something naughty, as befits a witch's cat, but he knew how angry Inky would be. She might turn him into something awful – like a dog! Whispers **hated** dogs!

Powder thought it would be nice to go and visit Ghostly White before she went home again.

She peeped in through his window as she passed. Ghostly was tying a big pink bow round his pet mouse's neck.

"You're going to be the smartest mouse in town, Squeak," fussed the happy ghost.

Squeak loved the pretty bow. It matched her little pink paws, nose, ears and tail!

"Oh," sighed Powder Blue. "It looks like Ghostly will be going to the pet show, too. So he won't want to see me after all."

"I may as well go home again," muttered the little Blob. "I don't have a pet like the rest of them."

She was so sad, she sat down under a tree and began to sob. "Boo-hoo!" she cried.

The noise was heard by a little bluebird who had been sitting in the branches of the tree above Powder's head.

"Oh dear, oh dear, oh dear! What's going on here?" he cheeped.

"I d-don't have a p-pet to t-take t-to the p-pet sh-show!" blubbed Powder. "Everyone else has one!"

"Well, we can soon fix that. You can take **me**! I'm not doing anything today anyway," he chirped.

"Really?" asked Powder Blue. "You **are** the right colour!"

The bluebird preened his feathers till he looked his best, then he perched on Powder's hand.

She walked proudly into the show where the other entrants were already waiting to be judged.

"When did you get a pet bird?" asked Ghostly.

"Just a little while ago," smiled Powder.

"He's a smart little fellow!" cackled Inky.

He was so smart that King Royal Blue judged him best and gave Powder the first prize.

She was the happiest Blob at the show! Meanwhile, Squeak just wanted to go home. She didn't like the way Whispers was licking his lips!

Witch Winkle

Witch Winkle and Wendy Wilson are flying high in the sky!

1. Can you count all the stars in this picture?

2. How many people are looking out of the window?

3. There are five bats hidden in this picture. Can you find them?

4. Where are these faces in the picture?

Diana's Ducklings

1 — Diana lived in the country with her mummy and daddy. At the bottom of their garden was a shallow stream. Diana would often paddle in it.

2 — One day, Diana decided to build a dam. She collected twigs and stones and piled them up in the water. The birds were puzzled by Diana's game.

3 — Later, Diana spotted a nest of baby ducks. "I'd love to play with them," sighed Diana, "but I don't imagine their mother would let me near them."

4 — One day, though, it began to rain very heavily. Diana's dam began to cause problems in the stream. The water ran fast and flooded over the banks.

5 — When the rain stopped, Daddy, Mummy and Diana all went outside. Diana rushed to the stream, just in time to see the ducklings being carried away.

6 — "Oh, no!" shouted Diana. "Save them, Daddy." But the nest had passed before he could reach it. The nest sped on until, luckily, it came to rest on Diana's dam.

7 — "Your dam may have caused a flood," chuckled Daddy, "but it certainly saved those baby ducks. Mrs Duck **will** be pleased with you, Diana."

8 — Daddy was right. From then on, Mrs Duck allowed her babies to play with Diana every day. She knew they would be safe with their new playmate.

Speedy Spinning Top

Speedy the spinning top sat all alone in a dusty attic, feeling very sorry for himself. It had been a very long time since anyone had played with him.

"I wish someone would come and take me outside for a nice game," he sighed. "It's very lonely up here — and dark, too."

Then, almost as if answering Speedy's wish, the attic door creaked open and a man came in, followed by a lady and then a little girl. But then the lady said something that made Speedy tremble.

"Look at this rubbish!" she said. "Well, we'll have to get rid of it all when we move in tomorrow."

Speedy didn't sleep a wink that night. Next morning, he heard the door open again and the little girl, whose name was Anna, came in with a big brush. She started to sweep the floor, getting into all the corners. Suddenly, she swept up Speedy and he was whisked across the floor!

"What's that?" Anna asked when she saw him.

Anna's daddy came in to see what she was doing. He picked up the little top and the whip which lay on the floor, too.

"Goodness! It's an old-fashioned top," gasped Daddy. "It's practically an antique!"

"Show me how it works!" cried Anna.

But Daddy wasn't sure, so he asked Anna's grandad.

Speedy was so excited! He was taken out into the garden, where Anna's grandad had a go at making Speedy spin by using the whip. After a couple of tries, Speedy was happily spinning around.

"Let me try!" giggled Anna. She **loved** the way Speedy whizzed round, and Speedy was as happy as could be with his new owner.

Next morning, Anna was due to start at her new school. She wasn't looking forward to it. She popped Speedy into her schoolbag as she left. "I'll play with you at lunchtime," she said.

Anna felt rather lonely at school because she didn't know anyone and, at lunchtime, she took out Speedy and began to play.

"Hey! Look at this!" cried one of her classmates. "What a cool toy! Show us how it works."

Soon all the class wanted to play with Speedy, and Anna had made lots of new friends.

"You're the best toy in the world!" laughed Anna. And Speedy blushed!

Polly

Merry Christmas

Happy Christmas

1- Polly Penguin lives in Snowland with her chums, Suki Seal, Peter Polar Bear and Rodney Reindeer. It was nearly Christmas and Polly was out shopping.

2- She was looking for gifts for her friends, but everything was too expensive. "I don't have enough money to buy anything really nice," she sighed.

ICES

MOULDING KIT

3- Then Polly passed the ice cream parlour. "I've got lots of novelty ice cream for Christmas," said the owner. "Novelty ices... I wonder," thought Polly.

4- She hurried home and looked out her modelling kit and a big jug of water. "I'll **make** my presents this year," she chuckled. "They'll be very special!"

5- On Christmas morning, there was a knock on the door and Polly found her three best friends standing outside. "Merry Christmas!" they called happily.

6- "Come in!" Polly smiled. Then to their surprise, she went straight over to her freezer! "Your gifts are in here," she told them shyly. "I hope you like them!"

7- There were smiles all round when they opened up their parcels. Inside were garden **ice gnomes**, complete with gift bows! "That's really unusual!" cried Suki.

8- "I'm glad you like them," smiled the little penguin. "Now, let's pop them back in the freezer while we tuck in to Christmas pudding and mince pies! Yum!"

MAKE YOUR OWN

CHRISTMAS CALENDAR

Calendar

Like Polly, you can make your own Christmas gifts. How about a pretty calendar? We'll show you how to do it.

YOU WILL NEED

- Card
- Paste
- Scissors
- Small piece of ribbon
- An old Christmas card
- Calendar tag

WHAT TO DO

Cut out the picture from the front of a Christmas card and stick it to a larger sheet of plain card, leaving a border of about 25mm all round. You can decorate the border with a pretty pattern.

When you've done that, attach the calendar tag to the bottom of the card with ribbon and paste another piece of ribbon to the top of the card to make a hanger for it. You can use some sticky tape on the back to hold the ribbon more firmly in place.

Now your calendar is ready. It will make a lovely present for Mum, Dad or Granny!

The Runaway

RASCAL was a little tan and white dog. He lived with Rosie and her mummy and daddy in a house which had a big garden. But Rascal was always trying to escape from Rosie's garden.

"Oh, Rascal, you are a scamp!" Rosie sighed as she brought him back home one day. "It's very dangerous to go off all by yourself!"

Now Rascal had a special pal. It was Tom, the milkman. Sometimes Tom let Rascal sit in the milk-float with him as he went on his rounds.

"You must stay in the float while I go to the houses with the milk," Tom told him.

The doggy didn't mind. Some of Tom's customers used to come out and see him. They all made a fuss of Rascal.

"This is great," Rascal thought, as he was driven back home.

2 — Every morning, Rascal sat by the garden gate waiting for Tom. But, one day, Tom didn't turn up.

Then Rascal noticed something. The garden gate was open.

"Now there's a bit of luck!" Rascal thought. "I can go out on my own!"

3 — Rascal shot through the gate and scampered off down the road. Soon he came to some shops.

"Something smells nice," Rascal thought, sniffing the air outside the baker's shop.

"Shoo! Off you go!" called the baker when he saw Rascal. The little doggy ran away quickly.

"I'm hungry and I would like a drink of water," he sighed. "It's a pity that man wouldn't let me stay and have something to eat in his shop."

4 — Just then, Rascal came to a big supermarket where he spotted a lady with a big bag of shopping. Right on top of her bag were some sausages.

"Mmm," he thought, licking his lips, "I could eat a tasty sausage!"

Just then, a bus came along and drove through a big puddle. Splash! Poor Rascal was soaked!

"Rosie always dries me when I get wet," he thought. "Maybe this lady will dry me instead."

5 — Rascal followed the lady to her house and trotted up the drive after her. Then the lady spotted him.

"What a scruffy dog!" she cried. "Well, you can't come into **my** house — you'll frighten the cat!"

Poor Rascal padded away. "I want to go home," he sighed. "I'm tired of this adventure."

6 — Later, Rascal saw something that cheered him up. It was a milk-float! The doggy peeped inside, but Tom, his milkman pal, wasn't there.

"Tom will take me home when he comes back," Rascal thought, as he settled down to sleep.

7 — But, when he woke up, Rascal **did** get a shock! It **wasn't** Tom who was driving.

"Hello," said the kind milkman, as he stroked Rascal's head. "I'm always finding strays. I'll take you to the dog pound. Maybe your owner will come to collect you."

"I hope so!" Rascal thought in a panic.

Rascal didn't like the dog pound. He was put in a cage with lots of other stray dogs.

"I wish I was back home with Rosie," Rascal howled.

That night, Rascal dreamed that Rosie had come to collect him. It was a lovely dream.

8 — But then, when he woke in the morning, Rosie **had** come to collect him!

"I don't think I'll escape again in a hurry," thought the doggy. "From now on, I'll be happy to stay at home with Rosie."

How to play

- First of all, each player will need a coloured counter - or a brightly wrapped sweet.
- Roll a dice and the highest throw starts.
- On the way to the Christmas feast, you'll come across obstacles and helpful rewards.
- The winner is the first person to reach the dinner table. You must throw the exact number to finish. When you do, you get to eat everyone else's sweets! Have fun!

15 Dog steals sweets from the Christmas tree. Chase him back two spaces.

16

17 Find last year's Christmas crackers in the cupboard. Roll the dice again!

14

18

Finish

26

25 Forget to cook the chipolatas. Go back two spaces.

19

20 Kitty steals the cream. Whip some more and miss a go

24

23

21

22 Find the turkey wishbone. Go on two spaces.

Silly Milly

1 - Silly Milly is always in trouble. Just before Christmas, while out shopping with Mummy, Milly saw Santa's Grotto in a big store.

2 - Milly couldn't wait to visit Santa but, before the silly girl could get inside, she tangled herself in the antlers of a reindeer.

3 - When Milly finally made it into the grotto, she tripped over a pile of presents and almost knocked poor Santa off his seat!

4 - Once Santa had asked Milly what she would like for Christmas, he told her to choose a present from the tree.

5 - "This one, I think," said Milly as she grabbed a present. However, the gift was stuck, and Milly pulled the tree over.

6 - When Mummy returned to the grotto, there was no sign of Milly. " I wonder where the silly girl can be!" she puzzled.

7 - Mummy popped inside and, when she spotted Milly tied up in Santa's sack, she just had to laugh. "Trouble?" asked Mummy.

8 - "I'm sorry," sighed Santa, "but Milly caused **so** much trouble that I couldn't think what else to do with her!"

Witch Winkle

It's party time for Witch Winkle and all her friends!

1. How many masks can you count?

2. Can you find six small spiders hiding in this picture?

3. Where are these creatures in this picture?

Jessica's Fancy

Jessica was staying with her granny and grandpa for a holiday. One day, as they were having lunch, there was a knock on the door.

Jessica and Grandpa went to answer it and found Katie, the girl from next door, standing there.

"Hello," smiled Katie. "I've come to see if Jessica would like to come to my party this afternoon."

"Oh, thank you. I'd love that!" replied Jessica. "Is it a special kind of party?"

"It's really a fancy dress party," explained Katie, "but if you haven't got a costume, it doesn't matter. Just come as you are."

"All right - I'll be there," Jessica said with a smile.

2- After Katie left, Jessica and Grandpa went back to their lunch.

"I wish I had something to dress up in. I'll look a bit out of place," sighed Jessica. "I didn't think to bring anything like that with me."

"Never mind," smiled Grandpa. "How would you like to help me in the garden until it's time for your party?"

"Oh, yes please," Jessica replied, and she hurried to finish her lunch.

"There's no need to rush," Granny told her. "Grandpa has to get changed into his gardening clothes first."

When he came downstairs, he was dressed in a torn jacket and patched trousers and he had a battered old hat on his head.

"Oh, Grandpa!" laughed Jessica. "You **do** look funny dressed like that."

"I know," her grandpa agreed, "but these old clothes are just right for gardening."

Dress

3- Jessica put on her jacket and wellies, then she and Grandpa went out into the garden. Grandpa pointed to some tall plants.

"We need to tie up these plants," he explained. "Let's see if we can find any canes."

They looked in the garden shed and found some in a corner.

"What shall we use to tie the plants to the canes?" asked Jessica.

Grandpa laughed and took a ball made of tied-up lengths of string from his pocket.

"I never throw away string - it always comes in handy," he told her.

They had a busy time tying the plants to the canes. Jessica enjoyed helping Grandpa, even though it was messy work.

"That should make them grow nice and straight," said Grandpa when they'd finished. "Let's go inside and have tea and buns before it's time for your party."

4- When they went back into the house, they found Granny making little furry mice.

"These are lovely!" Jessica cried.

"I'm making them to sell at the village fete," Granny told her. "Now, I'll make some tea, and afterwards you can change into your party clothes."

Then, looking at Grandpa, she laughed, "I think **you'd** better get changed right now. You look like an old scarecrow!"

Grandpa looked thoughtful, then plonked his hat on Jessica's head.

"Not bad," he chuckled. "Now let's see how my jacket fits."

"It's too big and the sleeves are much too long," Jessica protested, puzzled.

"That's where my string will come in handy again," said Grandpa. "I'll tie up the sleeves with string - and you can go to the party dressed as a **scarecrow**."

"You **are** clever!" said Jessica. "But what about trousers?"

"I could sew some bright patches to your play trousers," suggested Granny.

5- While Granny stitched a red patch to one leg of Jessica's play trousers and a spotty yellow patch to the other, Grandpa went to the garden shed and and collected two short canes.

When he came back, he pushed them up the sleeves of his old jacket which Jessica was wearing. Then Granny tied Jessica's hair in bunches with some more of Grandpa's string.

"Now, what shall I give you to take as a present?" asked Granny.

"One of your furry little mice would make a lovely gift," suggested Grandpa. "And we'll tie one to Jessica's hat. That will make her look even **more** like a scarecrow!"

Jessica had a lovely time at the party and she was full of chatter when she came home.

"Katie loved the little mouse and I won a prize for my costume," she told Grandpa.

"I'm not surprised," he laughed. "You're the best scarecrow I've ever seen!"

STAR SEARCH

All these Twinkle stars are in this book. Can you find them hiding in our wordsearch? They can read up, down, backwards or forwards. Letters can be used more than once. Good luck!

BEN ● DIANA ● ELFIE ● NURSE NANCY
PATCH ● POLLY ● RASCAL ● SAMMY
SARA ● SCAMP ● SIDNEY ● SILLY MILLY
SPEEDY ● THE BLOBS ● WITCH WINKLE

A	E	L	K	N	I	W	H	C	T	I	W
N	D	F	H	G	J	S	I	D	N	E	Y
U	S	E	Y	D	E	E	P	S	O	P	S
R	C	B	M	I	K	S	T	B	U	Q	I
S	A	R	A	L	U	V	W	O	E	R	L
E	M	C	S	A	X	P	O	L	L	Y	L
N	P	M	Y	N	E	B	D	B	F	E	Y
A	N	Z	B	A	C	F	H	E	I	G	M
N	A	I	P	I	S	M	U	H	E	N	I
C	K	Q	J	D	V	X	A	T	O	C	L
Y	R	L	T	W	L	A	C	S	A	R	L
P	A	T	C	H	B	D	S	A	M	M	Y

Animal Magic

Mmm... this is 'welly' comfortable.

I'm very moo-sical, you kno

I think I'm really supposed to wear this on my head

These jeans are definitely too big!

Elfie

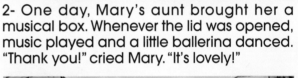

1- Elfie lives in Mary's doll's house. Only Mary's dog, Poochie, knows about the little elf. When Elfie makes things happen, Mary thinks that it's caused by magic!

2- One day, Mary's aunt brought her a musical box. Whenever the lid was opened, music played and a little ballerina danced. "Thank you!" cried Mary. "It's lovely!"

3- Mary showed the musical box to Poochie. He wasn't the only one who was interested. Elfie was watching, too. "I'd like to play with that," he thought.

4- Elfie didn't have to wait long. Mary was going to see her friend, Susan. Poochie watched her go down the garden path. "Now's your chance, Elfie," he wuffed.

5- When Elfie opened the box, however, he was most upset to discover that the ballerina wouldn't dance. "She's got stuck when the lid closed," he thought.

6- Elfie knew what to do, though. He went to the playroom and got his little box of tools. "I'll have it fixed by the time Mary comes back," he told Poochie.

7- Soon Elfie had bits and pieces of the musical box spread all over the floor. He was still putting it back together when Poochie barked a warning.

8- "Mary's coming back and bringing Susan with her," wuffed the dog. "Mary will want to show Susan the musical box," gasped Elfie, "and it's not ready yet!"

9- "There's only one thing for it, then," said Elfie. He quickly hid his toolbox and the ballerina before he clambered into the musical box. What **was** he doing?

10- "Now you must help, Poochie," Elfie called. "Give Mary such a welcome that Susan will look at the musical box on her own." Poochie was very puzzled.

11- When the girls came in, Poochie bounded over to Mary. "Well, you **are** pleased to see me," she laughed. Susan went over to look at the musical box.

12- "It's **very** unusual," she cried. And it was. For, in place of the dancing ballerina was Elfie! "I'll replace the ballerina later," he chuckled. "Mary will never know!"

Busy Bees!

Can you lead the busy bees through their hive to the door?

start

door

Sidney's Sad Secret

Sidney, the little steam train, lived in the goods yard of Rambletown Railway. Back and forth he chugged merrily all day, pulling coal trucks and passenger carriages.

Little Sidney wasn't afraid of hard work. He often pulled goods trucks which were twice as heavy as himself. But Sidney had a secret. There was one thing he was **afraid** of - he didn't like the dark.

Every night when Mr Green, Sidney's driver, backed him into his little shed and turned off the lights, little Sidney began to tremble. No matter how often he told himself he was being silly, Sidney was **still** afraid!

Quite often the moon would try to shine into the shed and make it brighter, but not even **this** helped the little engine.

One morning, Mr Green arrived to drive Sidney into the yard.

"This is a special day, Sidney," he beamed. "The big engine is broken and **you** are to pull the passengers into town."

Sidney could hardly believe it.

"**Me**?" he gasped. "Pull carriages?"

Everything was going well, when a tunnel loomed up in front of him! All the little engine could see was a big black hole - and he didn't want to go into it!

Sidney slammed on his brakes, sending coal flying from his box and jolting the passengers in the coaches.

"What's wrong?" gasped Mr Green, mopping his brow.

"It's d . . . dark in there!" tooted Sidney in a trembling voice. " I d . . . don't like the d . . . dark!"

Mr Green tried to coax the little engine into the tunnel. But no matter how he tried, Sidney would not budge. In the end, another steam engine came to pick up the passengers, and Sidney was backed into a siding.

Sidney **was** upset. He didn't mean to cause the passengers any trouble, but he just couldn't bring himself to chug into the darkness.

Sidney sat in the siding all day. Soon the noise of the trains grew quieter. It began to grow dark and the little engine became very uneasy.

Just then, a shadowy figure appeared. "Oh, no!" gasped the little engine. "It's a ghost! It's come to get me!"

"Don't be so silly, Sidney," chuckled the figure. "It's **me**, Mr Green, and I've got a present for you."

Mr. Green opened a large box, and began to fix something to Sidney's funnel. "There you are," he said, when he was finished. "Now you don't need to be afraid of the dark."

Sidney couldn't believe his eyes when Mr Green switched on a shiny new lamp, and the countryside around him lit up.

After that, the little train went **everywhere** with his light switched on, and he was never afraid to go into tunnels again.

Father Christmas FUN

You can colour this picture with coloured pens or pencils.

Which lead is pinned to Bobby's collar?

Answer: B will lead you to Bobby

Can you find six differences between these two pictures?

Lead Santa through the maze to his sack of toys.

Join the dots to see this Christmas toy.

Rearrange the letters to see what this is.

Answer : STOCKING

Which two reindeer are the same?

Answer :
1 and 4

Sara and Sam

Sara Bright was excited. She had been chosen to play in the netball team. Daddy and Sam were going to watch her play against another team in the sports centre.

Daddy drove Sara and Sam to the centre. Next to the sports centre there was a big sweet shop.

"Can I go to that shop and buy some sweets?" Sam asked.

"All right!" said Daddy. "But you'll have to be quick or Sara will be late for her netball game."

Sam spent a long time trying to decide which sweets to buy.

"Hurry up, Sam," moaned Sara. "The game will start without me if I'm not there on time."

Sam finally chose some fudge and an unusual lollipop, shaped like a whistle.

"It works just like a real whistle, too, Sara," grinned Sam. "I'll save it till later."

Sara wasn't really interested in Sam's lollipop. She just wanted to get to the sports centre in time for her game.

But Sara was **very** disappointed when she arrived at the sports centre and found that the netball game had been cancelled.

"I've forgotten to bring a whistle," explained Sara's teacher, Mrs Robb. "I can't referee the netball game without a whistle."

"You could use my whistling lollipop," suggested Sam.

"What a clever boy," smiled Mrs Robb. "Thank you, Sam."

So, thanks to Sam's whistling lollipop, the netball game could go ahead after all.

"Peep, peep, peep!" tooted Mrs Robb.

"Now I'm glad Sam took his time choosing his sweets," laughed Sara.

Clever Scamp

Shelley the tortoise opened her eyes slowly and gave a wide yawn.

"Mmm," she sighed, "that was a good winter sleep. Now I'm ready to get up."

Shelley belonged to Claire and John. Every winter, they put Shelley in a cosy box of straw. She hibernated till the warmer weather was near. The children also had a puppy called Scamp. He heard Shelley moving about in her box and bounded over to see her.

"Hello, Shelley!" he called. "Nice to see you again."

"Hello, Scamp," yawned Shelley. "It's nice to be awake again."

Slowly, Shelley climbed out of her box.

"Ooh, I feel a bit stiff after all these weeks asleep," sighed Shelley.

"What you need is some exercise," woofed Scamp. "Let's go for a walk."

"But it will be too cold outside for me," said Shelley.

Scamp ran off and found some things to keep Shelley warm - four woolly egg cosies for her feet and another one for her head!

Outside, Shelley and Scamp met Ginger, the next door neighbour's cat.

"Hello, Shelley!" called Ginger. "Good to see you. Where are you two going?"

"We're taking a walk to the woods so that Shelley can ease off the aches and pains of her long sleep," explained Scamp. "Do you want to come with us?"

"Yes, that would be nice," purred Ginger. "I was wondering what to do with myself."

The threesome set off towards the woods. They had lots to chat about. Scamp and Ginger told Shelley everything that had happened while she had been asleep.

"A new family has moved into the house next to mine," said Ginger. "They've got a dog, but he's not as nice as Scamp!"

As they walked along the path, Shelley thought she could hear the sound of crying nearby.

"Listen!" Shelley called to her friends. "Can you hear that?"

Ginger and Scamp stopped and listened. They could hear it, too.

"It's coming from behind that tree," barked Scamp.

They all went to see who it was, and found a tearful little squirrel sitting there.

"Why are you crying, little fellow?" asked Shelley kindly.

"I've lost my store of nuts!" gulped the squirrel who was called Nutty. "Before I went to sleep for the winter, I hid some nuts so that I would have something to eat when I woke up. But now I can't remember where they are and I'm **so** hungry!"

Two little birds flew down. They offered to fly around in search of the hidden store, but they had no luck, either.

Then a boy and girl came along the path in front of them.

Here is a picture for you to colour.

"Look!" whispered Ginger. "They've got a bag of nuts."

"Why don't we ask them if they'll give them to Nutty?" piped up Scamp.

"We can't," explained Shelley. "They wouldn't understand us. To them, we can only make sounds like barking, miaowing or squeaking. We'll have to think of something else."

"What if we do something that might make them give us some of the nuts?" suggested Scamp.

He ran over to the boy and tugged at his trouser leg.

"What do you want?" asked the boy whose name was Jamie.

"Right," said Scamp to his chums, "now that we've got his attention, do something."

Ginger didn't know what to do, so she started miaowing and rubbing up against the little girl's legs. That didn't seem to work. Nutty tried. He scampered up and down a tree and jumped from branch to branch.

"What a cute cat and a sweet squirrel!" laughed the little girl, Becky.

But they were no closer to getting some nuts for Nutty. Then it was Scamp's turn.

"What can I do?" he wondered. "Ah, I know!"

Scamp put on his most appealing face, sat up on his hind legs and begged. It worked!

"Aw!" said Becky. "Let's give the clever doggy and his friends some of these nuts."

As she threw the nuts to them, the clever animals tried to catch them. That made Jamie and Becky laugh.

"Aren't they funny?" cried Jamie. "Throw some more to them!"

When the bag was empty, the children left to walk home, still laughing.

"That was fun!" giggled Ginger.

"Good exercise, too!" smiled Shelley.

Scamp looked at the pile of nuts they had collected.

"These should keep you going for a while," he wuffed to the happy squirrel.

"Thank you, all of you, but especially you, Scamp," said Nutty. "If it hadn't been for you, I would still be hungry!"

"I think it's time we went home," said Ginger. "All this talk about food has made me feel quite peckish!"

"Yes, and Claire and John will want to see you, Shelley," added Scamp, "because they'll notice you're not in your box any more. They'll be home from school in a little while."

"I think I'll need another sleep to get over all this excitement," said Shelley.

"Ha, ha!" laughed Nutty. "See you all the next time you're out for a walk."

"Yes, but make sure you know where your food store is next time we see you!" chuckled Scamp.

Sammy Skates

1 - "Help!" cried Walter Wagtail, as he landed on the ice with a bump! "It's no use," said Molly Moorhen. "We'll never be able to skate." Sammy Snowman just laughed.

2 - "Maybe I can teach you," he said. "But how?" quacked Donna Duck, looking at his feet. "You're frozen to the ground." Sure enough, Sammy couldn't move.

3 - "Oh, dear!" said Sammy, tearfully. "I did so want to go skating." Just then, Robbie Robin flew down. Sammy told him his problem, and the little bird flew off.

4 - Robbie went to find Harry Hare and Betty Bunny, who were playing with their sledge. "There's something I want you to do," he said. "Will you help me, please?"

5 - Harry and Betty were happy to help Robbie and positioned their sledge at the top of the hill. Sammy was puzzled. What were his little friends up to?

6 - The sledge went whizzing down the hill. Just as it reached the bottom, the furry friends jumped off. But the sledge kept on going, right in the direction of Sammy!

7 - Instead of knocking the snowman over, though, the sledge freed him from the ground, and carried him on to the pond. Soon Sammy was zooming round the ice.

8 - Donna Duck grabbed Sammy's scarf, and all the chums followed on. "I've helped you to skate, after all," laughed Sammy. "And it's the best fun I've had in ages!"

Nurse Nancy's always on the go,
She cares for all the toys,
Until they're well enough to head
Back home with girls and boys.

Poor Teddy has an injured eye,
While Dolly's foot is sore.
Young Baby hurt her head and arm
By falling on the floor.

With both her feet in plaster, Sue
Sits in her special chair.
But all will soon be better, thanks
To Nancy's loving care.

And as it's Christmas, Nancy's baked
Her friends a special treat.
She's made some yummy mincemeat pies
For everyone to eat.

So if your doll or teddy's sick,
Don't panic or despair.
Go to the Dollies Hospital
And Nancy will be there.

She'll give the patients lots of love,
And see they all get rest.
'Cause when it comes to nursing
Nancy clearly is the best!